LI

Living With PMT

SHIRLEY JEBB

KINGSWAY PUBLICATIONS
EASTBOURNE

First published 1991

Biblical quotations are from the
New International Version © 1973, 1978, 1984 by the
International Bible Society, unless otherwise marked.
Amplified = The Amplified Bible, Old Testament
© Zondervan Publishing House, 1962, 1964
New Testament © Lockman Foundation 1954,
1958.

Phillips = The New Testament in Modern English by
J B Phillips, © J B Phillips 1958, 1960, 1972.

GNB = Good News Bible © American Bible Society 1976,
published by the Bible Societies and Collins.

British Library Cataloguing in Publication Data

Jebb, Shirley
Living with PMT.
I. Title
618.172

ISBN 0–86065–953–4

Printed in Great Britain for
KINGSWAY PUBLICATIONS LTD
1 St Anne's Road, Eastbourne, E Sussex BN21 3UN by
Clays Ltd, St. Ives plc
Typeset by J&L Composition Ltd, Filey, North Yorkshire

Contents

Acknowledgements

I would like to thank all the people who have shared so honestly with me, the people who have been patient with me, and the medical experts who have sent me information, especially Dr Michael Brush of St Thomas' Hospital. In addition, a special thanks to all those in New Covenant Church who have helped with the content of this book, and Michelle Bass for the illustrations.

1

What's the Battle Anyway?

'For I do not understand my own actions—I am baffled, bewildered' (Rom 7:15 AMPLIFIED).

I am myself again and I wonder what all the fuss was about and whether it's worth writing about the subject.

Yes, that's how we all feel when the pre-menstrual tension has passed and our hormones have settled down again to normal. Maybe you can identify with this yourself or have a friend with such symptoms; if so, you will realise that these issues cannot be ignored. They really are a recurring problem for Christian women who want to live balanced, positive lives and help one another.

I am a pastor's wife, and many women have shared with me their hopes and fears in this realm. We have gathered data together to share our experiences, and our victories. Older women have confided that they wish they had been able to share when they were suffering in this way—and at the other end of the spectrum we see how we can prepare and help our daughters and understand their needs. This is one of the ways in which the older women can 'train the younger women' (Tit 2:3–5).

Our church has a lovely array of women's meetings. We began as a small prayer and share group, which outgrew first the manse and then the church hall; as we continued to grow we felt God say to us through Nehemiah, 'Build the wall near your house ...' So we broke up into area groups around the town, with crèches nearby and from time to time we enjoy meeting together in the evenings. The members of these groups have been my 'think tank'.

The fact that this is a corporate sharing of experiences gives me confidence to write. We looked over the questionnaire on pages 17 and 19 for a few months and what we discovered was added to my research of the past few years. Many women's magazines write about the matter these days, and there are several recent books on the subject. We want to share what we have learned as Christian women seeking to practise Christ's teaching and to live by the word of God and seeing its relevance to our needs.

I will outline first the symptoms and then some solutions. Let me emphasise that this is not medically based research, although we have gathered medical advice. (The bibliography on pages 89–90 includes books which contain medical details.) Rather, we want to see our conquering in the light of the whole person—body, soul and spirit.

In the main we are talking about pre-menstrual tension, or Pre-Menstrual Syndrome, but as these behaviour patterns are caused by hormonal imbalances, they can occur with post-natal depression, before and during the menopause, and also in the time leading up to the start of menstruation in young girls. The physical problems such as the cramp pains (spasmodic dysmenorrhoea) and also the achiness that lasts for several days (congestive dysmenorrhoea) have the same cause and can be alleviated by following the same advice.

The main hormones that come out of balance are progesterone, oestrogen and prolactin. The last of these is a hormone that dampens down our response to stress and makes us feel less anxious. The symptoms are extremely common in women aged thirty to forty-five. A medical journal says,

> The affected individual is often full of restless energy, cleaning the house when it is already spotless, fussing and nagging children, worrying when there is no need. The husband cannot understand the periodic outbursts and moods; the resulting quarrels make the situation worse. It is the imaginative women 'living on her nerves' who is most likely to suffer.

I have many case histories which could illustrate the sufferings of the women and families caused by these hormonal imbalances, but as sensitive believers I don't think we need to use space to go into detail.

We want to be better informed and prepared—unlike one of Joyce Grenfell's characters who said her friend had been to a lecture at the WI with her niece. 'It was on hormones, not very nice things, hormones. But did you know we were all supposed to have them? No? It was news to me too—I don't think I've got any!'

The majority of doctors recognise this as a definite condition that can be diagnosed by keeping a monthly chart which will show distinct physical and emotional changes. Often reassurance comes just by realising it is a chemical imbalance and that a high percentage of women suffer from it to one degree or another. It can vary in length from a day or two to half the month. Often it begins by a tensing of the muscles which seems to stem from an unjustified sense of anxiety. Fluid retention sometimes occurs which results in weight increase, as the fluid collects in damaged or weak areas. A three-day headache is sometimes present and these days are characterised by a sense of restless energy, coupled with a panic that things won't get done, interspersed with lethargic feelings and confusion.

Often there is a complete change of personality from a placid, easy-going nature to one that is intense, hostile and quarrelsome. We in fact become female Jekyll and Hydes. One doctor has a theory that women's personalities are 'oestrogen backed' and believes that lively, outgoing women have this mood change because of low oestrogen. The same doctor believes that women who usually have low oestrogen anyway don't have such violent mood changes during the month and have a calmer transition through the menopause. I have also read that it is the imaginative, creative woman who suffers, if that's any comfort!

Queen Victoria apparently suffered from it and her husband was relieved each time she was pregnant! Courtiers were known to flee from her presence, not walking backwards with reverence as they should.

One woman says that she becomes irritable and intolerant; she can't let doctrinal differences go when she feels like this, and has to argue! Another reports that her driving instructor said that if she ever did pass her test she should never take her car onto the road during the time of her pre-menstrual tension; another says that she presents a hazard simply by riding her bike!

I have read that the majority of crimes by women are committed at their times of tension. Baby battering occurs more frequently then, and female students have a lower examination pass rate at such times. Miscarriages may be more common in women who experience severe PMT.

Dr Katharina Dalton has done a great deal of research in this area. She proposes this definition: 'A wide variety of regularly recurring physical and psychological symptoms which occur at the same time in the pre-menstrual period of each cycle.' She explains that women who have had a hysterectomy also suffer, because the menstrual clock in their brains cannot be cut out by surgery; the

Clumsy Syndrome

build-up of tensions does not have the release which the normally menstruating woman experiences. She was consulted in a case where a barmaid had been involved in a murder. The woman's father found her diary, which showed a regular pattern of hostility. Dr Dalton recognised this as a result of PMT and a clause of diminished responsibility was considered; this has now been included in our legal system. The French had that clause in their law last century!

In a recent paper on Christian Counselling, Dr Raju Abraham MRCP, one of the founders of the Association of Biblical Counsellors, says:

The premenstrual syndrome affects a great many women in varying degrees every month. The following points can be made from a Christian doctor's perspective:

1. Despite considerable research, our medical understanding is far from complete.
2. Medical treatment gives no consistent help to most people.
3. The symptoms vary in number and intensity from sufferer to sufferer. It is important to assess each person's symptoms individually and not generalise, or minimise.
4. It is a timed condition, ie occurs cyclically. Continuous symptoms throughout the monthly cycle should make one rethink.
5. PMT may be contributing to a person's other problems for which she may be seeking help.
6. Some of the symptoms of PMT like anxiety or irritability are particularly problematic because

they affect one's attitude, thinking and behaviour. The Christian counsellor can be crucial in helping that person to come through with honesty and integrity.

7. Husbands, family and friends can be very helpful resources for sufferers.

Does this section of Romans sum up the dilemma we are in?

My own behaviour baffles me. For I find myself not doing what I really want to do but doing what I really loathe. Yet surely if I do things that I really don't want to do it cannot be said that 'I' am doing them at all—it must be sin that has made its home in my nature. (And indeed I know from experience that the carnal side of my being can scarcely be called the home of good!) I often find that I have the will to do good but not the power. That is, I don't accomplish the good I set out to do and the evil I don't really want to do I find I am always doing. Yet if I do things that I don't really want to do then it is not, I repeat, 'I' who does them, but the sin which has made its home within me. When I come up against the Law I want to do good, but in practice I do evil. My conscious mind whole-heartedly endorses the Law, yet I observe an entirely different principle at work in my nature. This is in continual conflict with my conscious attitude and makes me an unwilling prisoner to the law of sin and death. In my mind I am God's willing servant, but in my own nature I am bound fast, as I say, to the law of sin and death. It is an agonising situation and who on earth can set me free from the clutches of my own sinful nature? I thank God there is a way out through Jesus Christ our Lord (Rom 7:15–25, PHILLIPS).

Questionnaire

'A garment of praise instead of a spirit of despair' (Is 61:3)

During the next few months consider this subject ready for group discussion. Do you have, or have you suffered from any of these symptoms? If not, find a friend who has and ask her to help in our research.

In what form does the hormone imbalance show itself?

Physical pain
Muscle stiffness
Headaches
Abdominal pain
Backache
Tiredness
General aches and
  pains
Water retention
Gain in weight
Skin disorders
Painful breasts
Feeling bloated
Spontaneous bruising
Dizziness
Fainting

Nausea
Cold sweats
Hot flushes
Greasy hair

Mental negativism
Crying spells
Loneliness
Anxiety
Restlessness
Irritability
Hostility
Depression
Mood swings
Misery

Cramp Syndrome

Criticalness

Feeling unattractive

Lack of concentration

Difficulty in sleeping

Forgetfulness

Confusion

Clumsiness

Indecision

Behavioural changes

Lowered performance

Take naps, stay in bed

Avoid social life

Loss of efficiency

Hyperactivity

Inner emotional
deadness

Loss of sex drive

Add anything else that is relevant, eg more breakages at this time? Driving performance lessened?

What practical solutions have you learnt that help to relieve the tension? Have you found any medical help, articles, books? Has your husband or a friend who knows you well any observations to make?

'Every test that you have experienced is the kind that normally comes to people. But God keeps his promise, and he will not allow you to be tempted beyond your power to remain firm; at the time you are put to the test, he will give you the strength to endure it, and so provide you with a way out' (1 Cor 10:13, GNB).

'We know that in all things God works for good with those who love him, those he has called according to his purpose' (Rom 8:28, GNB).

What have you learnt concerning living out the principles of the Kingdom and the government of God through these experiences? Have communications been weakened or strengthened? Have you learnt to praise God in everything? Is the fruit of the Spirit being developed?

2

Victory You Say?

'I thank God there is a way out through Jesus Christ' (Rom 7:25, PHILLIPS).

Jay Adams, a pastor who specialises in biblical counselling, has written many books and leaflets. In *A Personal Word to Women* he says: 'You don't have to become a tiger round the house once a month.' He goes on to say that it is rare for menstruation to cause such radical behaviour change that a woman may be relieved of responsibility for her actions. In most cases, he says, the monthly discomfort can do no more than present you with an occasion to sin. 'You must not allow it to become an excuse to become hostile, bitter, nasty, depressed, etc. While it is harder to control your attitudes and behaviour God holds you responsible to do so.'

Hard words, you say—and he is, of course, a man! But we all know in our hearts that this is right and the word of God supports this. We are conforming to the world if we explain and excuse ourselves in this way. Humanism can affect our thinking, and women's-liberation philosophy affects its outworking.

So what factors has the Lord put into our training as women of God so that he can give us the victory? 'The Lion of Judah shall break every chain and give us the victory again and again.'

We can learn to be victorious by:

Reading the Bible
Meditating on verses
Making Scripture memory a habit
Prayer and praise
Diet and exercise
Right attitude to authority
Training ourselves in positive thinking
Caring for others and also ourselves
Easing situations of stress
Sharing our need for support
Knowing that it will pass

I will enlarge on these later.

Self-pity, fear, resentment and unforgiveness are aspects from which a child of God wants to be free. If these are lurking in our hearts they will be exposed at this time of the month: we need deliverance from them, and in the properly functioning body of Christ there will be sisters to whom we can go for prayer and counsel on such matters. It may be that the whole situation is rooted in deep-seated fears which wise counsel will uncover and deal with. (Avoid intense counselling, though, at these bad times, and check this factor if you are counselling a distressed woman.)

There may be a root of resentment surrounding our womanhood, or an unfulfilled desire for motherhood, or even fear of pregnancy. Some young girls are wrongly prepared for the onset of menstruation, and deep in their memories some women have hurts and fears surrounding the circumstances of starting their periods.

In these cases the Spirit of God can enter them and heal. Our young girls need to be taught the wonder of our femininity and hormonal make-up and the sheer miraculous nature of our body that causes menstruation: 'Our daughters will be like pillars, carved to adorn a palace' (Ps 144:12). I don't think we should ever use the phrase 'the curse'. In Scripture this phrase refers to something far more serious than menstruation. As it says in the hymn 'Jesus shall reign where'er the sun':

> Where He displays His healing power
> Death and the curse are known no more.

The Fall of man, as described in Genesis 3, resulted in the curse of God upon us, but Christ bore the burden of our sins and carried the curse: 'Christ redeemed us from the curse of the law by becoming a curse for us, for it is written, "Cursed is everyone who is hung on a tree"' (Gal 3:13).

If, in spite of prayer and counsel, some of these difficult behaviour patterns recur, bear in mind that it can take eighteen months to work out new patterns or grooves of thinking and acting. The 'landing strip' in your mind that the enemy has so often used takes a while to be cultivated into the 'garden' of God's thoughts.

3
Spiritual Helps

'God is faithful; he will not let you be tempted beyond what you can bear' (1 Cor 10:13).

Pre-menstrual tension has a strange effect on our Christian lives. At this particular time of the month it is harder to read and get anything out of the word of God. It is harder to pray, it is harder to worship among his people and hear the word. That last sentence shows us the stamp of the enemy's activities in our lives as women and seems a continuation of the confrontation with Eve: 'I will greatly increase your pains in childbearing. With pain you will give birth to children. Your desire will be for your husband and he will rule over you' (Gen 3:16).

It seems that Satan, having once used woman to spoil God's plan, sees no reason why he shouldn't continue to do so. Women have often been at the heart of false sects; women have been the cause of much trouble in churches, and we are the first line of attack Satan would choose to use to bring down our husbands and leaders. But don't be discouraged! 'The one who is in you is greater than the one who is in the world' (1 Jn 4:4), and we see God at work in women to bring about his glorious purposes. 'The hand that rocks the cradle rules the world': our influence with our children can be regarded as a positive input we can make. It is also said, 'Behind every great man there is a woman': another area of positive opportunity. (I have dealt separately with the whole subject of our place in submission.)

John, in writing to Gaius says, 'Dear friend, I pray that you may enjoy good health and that all may go well with you, even as your soul is getting along well' (3 Jn 2). Everything I have read proves that it is a health factor we are contending with, but our souls can prosper in spite of health difficulties, and during our 'normal' times we must nourish our spiritual lives and not count on feelings when we are not ourselves.

We can look on this health matter and on any other trying circumstance as a chance to see God's all-sufficiency in action despite our circumstances. Acts 1:8 speaks of believers receiving power for witness. I believe women who have received the fullness of the Holy Spirit have added power to combat these spiritual difficulties and have a more buoyant faith. This power, described in Acts, gave the believers an opening in Jerusalem; translated to our situation that suggests our homes—the hardest place to live victoriously.

Psalm 122 talks of praying for the peace of Jerusalem and claims peace for within its walls. The next verse gives the key. 'Peace be within you.' We women set the atmosphere in the home, but within our 'Jerusalem' communications have to be open; the family will rally round and support us if our need is wisely shared.

We must ask for help when we are feeling under strain; we have to say 'no' to some assignments to preserve our strength for the less inspiring nitty-gritty tasks. Within family relationships Satan delights to get us preoccupied with our hurts and wounds, real or imagined, and that can distract us from the victory and healing that is possible. We damage ourselves by harbouring repressed resentments and smouldering self-pity. Our feelings must not dominate us. 'Great peace have they who love your law and nothing can make them stumble' (Ps 119:165).

In his book, *Don't Waste Your Sorrows*, Paul Bilheimer says that any adverse circumstances can be used by the Lord to train us, and to develop in us qualities that will enable us to reign over our circumstances.

John Newton, in this hymn, puts it rather graphically:

> I asked the Lord that I might grow,
> In faith, and love, and every grace,
> Might more of His salvation know,
> And seek more earnestly His face.

'Twas He who taught me thus to pray,
And He I trust has answered prayer;
But it has been in such a way
As almost drove me to despair.

I hoped that in some favoured hour
At once He'd answer my request;
And, by His love's constraining power,
Subdue my sins, and give me rest.

Instead of this, He made me feel
The hidden evils of my heart,
And let the angry powers of hell
Assault my soul in every part.

Yea, more, with His own hand He seemed
Intent to aggravate my woe,
Crossed all the fair designs I schemed,
Blasted my gourds, and laid me low.

'Lord, why is this?' I trembling cried,
'Wilt Thou pursue Thy worm to death?'
''Tis in this way,' the Lord replied
'I answer prayer for grace and faith.'

'These inward trials I employ,
From self and pride to set thee free,
And break thy schemes of earthly joy,
That thou mayest seek thy all in Me.'

There surely can be a place of abiding rest for
the daughters of the King—we who are appointed
to royalty! Esther had to spend months preparing
herself for the king with myrrh, which speaks
of death to self. This rest is an attitude of heart
—it comes after crossing the Jordan. When we

get our heart attitudes right, God gives us rest round about.

Feelings versus facts

> 'To be made new in the attitude of your minds ...' (Eph 4:23).

If we were to allow our feelings to dominate our actions at these times it would be fatal. We 'feel' as if God is far away, we 'feel' as if no one loves us or cares, we 'feel' as if we are failures.

Mood Swing Syndrome

We must put our trust in facts, and store up facts during the time when our feelings aren't running away with us, to draw on later. For instance, if you do anything successfully, praise the Lord for the skill he has given you and say to yourself, 'I'll remember this when I feel discouraged.'

As Christians, we no longer dwell in the City of Destruction; the fact is that *dis*couragement, *dis*may, *dis*ease, *dis*appointment, *dis*tress, are all part of the vocabulary of the past. The Celestial City offers righteousness, peace and joy in the Holy Ghost—however we feel.

So carry on with trusting God however you feel; worship him; offer a sacrifice of praise; read his word, for God honours and blesses obedience. Learn to have control over your own feelings. 'Like a city whose walls are broken down is a man who lacks self-control' (Prov 25:28). 'The wise woman builds up her house, but with her own hands the foolish one tears hers down' (Prov 14:1).

Bible meditation

> 'When your words came I ate them; they were my joy and my heart's delight' (Jer 15:16).

Meditation on Scripture is a means of having our minds renewed, and we should do it regularly, especially when we are feeling well. It is a way to garrison our hearts, and the Holy Spirit can draw on our store at times of need.

30

'It is good to choose positive Scriptures. If we are low in spirit we need to beware of judgmental Scriptures that would condemn us—such condemnation is not the voice of God' (Denis Clark). This is wise advice, though one long-suffering husband suggested that if such Scriptures kept coming to us, God could be speaking to us! If we read, 'The heart is deceitful above all things and beyond cure' (Jer 17:9), that may be the last straw when our self-esteem is at its lowest and we feel we've failed all round—true though the Scripture is! But the next verse: 'I the Lord search the heart and examine the mind' (Jer 17:10), is a very positive Scripture and can be applied to the matters we are talking about.

As a group of women trying to learn in the school of intercession, we meditated on 2 Chronicles 20:15, 'Be not afraid of the multitudes, the battle is the Lord's.' The problems we have been describing are like an overwhelming multitude but Watchman Nee says,

> Fight to get the victory and you have lost the battle from the very outset, for you are relinquishing ground that is yours. In the person of Jesus Christ, God has already conquered. What then is the secret? Simply look up and praise Him. The victory is all inclusive. It covers this situation, too. Then be at rest in the triumph already secured for you by God.

Sharon M. Sneed and Joe S. McIlhaney Jr say this in their book *PMS—What It Is and What You Can Do About It*:

31

Christian women are often confused about the possible relationship between their spiritual life and the presence of premenstrual tension. If you feel the comfort of the Holy Spirit during the good times of the month, you may wonder where that comfort is when you are at your wit's end and close to losing control during your premenstrual days. The answer is that the Spirit is still with you, but your body feels so bad that it is difficult to feel God's comfort. Many PMS women may have feelings of great anger or despair. Others feel quite ill, as if they had flu symptoms every fourth week. Some feel pushed to the outer edge of tolerance and control, while others are only mildly inconvenienced. Whatever the case may be, we would like to point out right now that PMS is not a spiritual problem. Whether or not a woman is in fellowship with God, she may experience symptoms of PMS so disturbing that she feels 'unspiritual' at the time. The fact is, she can still be in fellowship with God though her general feeling is one of discomfort, unrest, disharmony, and anger. Our attempt in pointing this out is to take away any unnecessary concern about your faith system. Don't let needless guilt over your lack of spirituality be an additional burden to carry as you deal with the physical problems of PMS. Remember that the vast majority of menstruating women, whether Christian or not, may be affected by PMS to some extent. You are definitely not an isolated statistic. And God has promised not to leave you 'comfortless'.

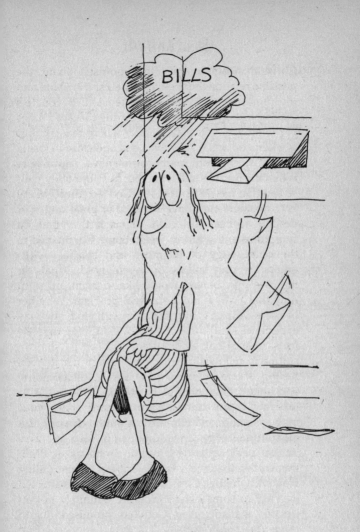

Impending Doom Syndrome

Scripture memory

'Do not let this Book of the Law depart from your mouth; meditate on it day and night, so that you may be careful to do everything written in it. Then you will be prosperous and successful' (Josh 1:8).

Storing God's word in our hearts through Scripture memory is a great safeguard. We can draw on it when a Bible is not available or it isn't convenient or possible to read one. As you learn a verse or passage think of what it means, and turn it into prayer, eg Psalm 23:1, 'The Lord is my shepherd': 'Thank you, Lord, that you are such a wonderful shepherd, that you died for me in order to be my shepherd,' etc.

If you use the Navigator topical memory verses, the card and wallet system, or ordinary cards, handbag size, or papers pinned around the house, these can remind you of the verse or passage. Brisk walking, with a glance at the card now and again, kills at least two birds with one stone!

Scripture memory can be valuable during the sleepless times of the pre-menstrual tension.

Submission

'Your beauty should be that of your inner self, the unfading beauty of a gentle and quiet spirit which is of great worth in God's sight' (1 Pet 3:4).

The symptoms of PMT test us, and reveal much that is in our hearts; yet when we see the beautiful standard and examples that are in God's word we know that we can settle for nothing less.

Again we go back to the Fall and see in Genesis 3:16 God's pronouncement at Eve's behaviour and action, 'And your desire shall be to your husband and he shall rule over you.' In our right frame of mind we do desire to please our husbands, or those whom God puts over us to cover and protect us—fathers, housegroup leaders, pastors—and we find their rule over us to be gentle and good. However, pre-menstrual tension can often produce hostility towards them, and negative attitudes so strong that they frighten us. That word 'desire', by the way, means 'impel and urge' in the original Hebrew. Very interesting!

Feminists are very quiet about this whole area of hormone imbalance. They don't want it recognised because of the repercussions for their cause. The issue of authority is crucial in these days when women are fighting to be 'free'. There is much misunderstanding about the role of man and woman, yet following the biblical pattern produces righteousness, peace and joy. God in his sovereign wisdom has positioned us so that the men are subject and answerable to him as Christ to the Father; we are loved and protected by the men as the church is by Christ, when it is called his bride.

'Wives, submit to your husbands as to the Lord' (Eph 5:22). 'The Christian is to respect this order remembering that God expects it to be followed not merely within the marriage and the home, but obviously within the Church and its worship and witness' (*The Head Covering* by Timothy Nelson).

Bill Gothard has a good definition of submission: 'The freedom to be creative under God-given ordained protection of divinely appointed authority.' Also, he defines a meek spirit as one free from fear and worry. Interestingly, the symptoms described on pages 17 and 19 are mainly characterised by fear and worry.

So we can recognise a pattern of warfare against the very principle of submission in relationships; having recognised it is half the battle.

We need to put on the whole armour of God so that our head (where our hormonal body-clock is situated), heart, loins (where the womb is situated), feet and every part of us is protected (Eph 6:11–17). We must snuggle under the covering and protection God has provided, admit our weakness and vulnerability and learn to dwell in the secret place of the Most High (Ps 91). We have seen relationships transformed as these principles have been applied and women have come to walk in freedom and fulfilment, having acknowledged their security.

A definition of submission is 'to yield humble and intelligent obedience to an ordained power or authority'. Christ did not cling to his legitimate rights, so nor should we. Proverbs 31 shows how fulfilled a submitted woman can be. You see this woman who is so satisfied; she is creative, enterprising, outgoing, honoured by her husband and children. Satan would spread the lie that we will lose our identity if we do things God's way, but we know that before God men and women are redemptively equal, but functionally different.

True submission is a means of physical, emotional, psychological and spiritual protection. When we go beyond our measure we put ourselves under an unnecessary strain. In submitting we release power for the Lord to work in us and those to whom we submit. No wonder Satan would say in our ear, 'Has God said . . .?' in the whole area of authority. It has been said that were Satan to tempt Eve today, he would not say, 'You shall be as God,' but, 'You shall be as man.'

4

The Medical Aspect

'I am fearfully and wonderfully made . . .'
(Ps 139:14).

There is widespread recognition of PMT as a medical problem, a chemical imbalance that can be altered, and one's family is the best judge of whether medical help should be sought. Doctors often prescribe tranquillisers, but these should be used only prayerfully and sparingly. Diuretics are useful to deal with the water retention: they are available on prescription but there is a danger that they may cause the body to lose valuable minerals. Herbal diuretics are less harmful, and some foods also act as natural diuretics. It has been suggested that limiting fluid intake to no more than four cups per day, and cutting down on salt may improve matters. Low progesterone levels suggest increased water and salt retention.

For tenseness of the muscles there are creams you can apply, and relaxation techniques you may learn. Professor Ronald Taylor from St Thomas' Hospital says that a doctor who simply listens and establishes a diagnosis can be of great value, and indeed this may be all that some women need. Dr Michael Brush has helped me a great deal by doing this and by supplying me with valuable information.

Muscle tension causes the muscle to clamp down on its own blood supply, so that toxic substances are not carried away. Their presence causes pain. The best remedy is exercise, though heat can also help. Another useful aid is Evening Primrose oil: research has shown that a deficiency in essential fatty acids could be the main underlying cause of PMT. Linoleic acid is the most important one, which needs to be converted into Gammalinolenic acid (GLA). With the processing of fat and the heating and cooling in food preparation, the function of the fat is changed and our bodies may become deficient in linoleic acid. One natural source of GLA is human breast milk, but otherwise the natural sources in other foods are very small. However, it is found concentrated to a high degree in the oil extracted from the Evening Primrose plant; other plant sources are being discovered.

Blocking agents get in the way of this process—such obstacles are found in rich, fatty foods high in cholesterol. Ageing, various weaknesses of the body, and deficiency in certain minerals such as zinc, all slow down this process of metabolism.

Vitamin B6 offers another line of treatment to help with this hormone imbalance (sometimes sold under the name Pyridoxine). However, it may be more helpful to take B6 in the context of the other B vitamins; this would be sold as B Complex. By the way, B6 can prevent cold sores, an added bonus.

Diagram to show Metabolic Pathway of Linoleic Acid

Step 1	Linoleic Acid
Step 2	↓ Gammalinolenic Acid (Evening Primrose Oil starts here)
Step 3	↓ Dihomo-Gammalinolenic Acid
Step 4	↓ Prostaglandin E1

Hormone Replacement Therapy (HRT) is well known in the United States and used widely. James Dobson in his book *Man to Man About Women* describes his own mother's suffering and the dramatic improvement which resulted from HRT. (She was going through the menopause and her oestrogen level was very low.) Some younger women have need for HRT because of the extreme symptoms of their PMT. Dr Katharina Dalton in her book *Once a Month* explains her theories of HRT: you would need to see a doctor to have your symptoms carefully observed before entering into a course of this treatment. Bear in mind that any artificial treatments can have an adverse effect on our immune system.

The Pre-Menstrual Tension Advisory Service, based in Brighton, suggests that sufferers from pre-menstrual tension can relieve their distressing symptoms by eating a diet high in particular vitamins and minerals. For example, women who suffer mood swings, irritability, anxiety and nervous tension should eat diets high in vitamin B6 and magnesium, as found in mackerel, egg yolk, cod, kale, kidneys, hazelnuts and tuna. Sufferers with symptoms of weight gain, breast tenderness, stomach bloating and swelling hands and feet need vitamin E, which is found in tomatoes, bananas, carrots, spinach, brown rice, roasted peanuts, olive oil and eggs; they also need some B6 and some magnesium. Increased appetite, cravings for sweet food, fatigue, headaches, depression, forgetfulness, crying, etc, can also be helped by eating more fresh fruit, salads, vegetables, proteins and complex carbohydrates.

This clinic will give personal advice concerning diet, and has also produced a video, 'PMT, A Self-Help Guide'. Their address is

The Pre-Menstrual Tension Advisory Service, PO Box 268, Hove, Sussex BN3 1RW.
Tel: Brighton (0273) 771366.

Food Binge Syndrome

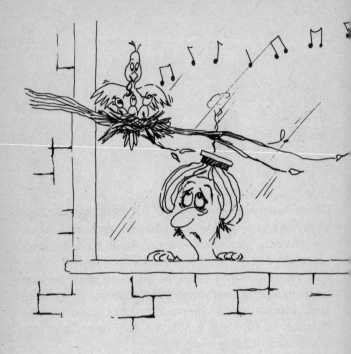

Headache Syndrome

5
Kingdom Eating

Good nutrition is essential for our well-being. There is a saying, 'We are what we eat', and there are various measures we can take to eat more correctly and so improve our overall health. Correct nutrition is important because our bodies have to spend extra energy digesting, absorbing and eliminating foods which are not good for us. Balance is the key word, so that we don't go overboard in extremes.

Progesterone levels which are low have an adverse effect on the sugar metabolism. Without enough progesterone the body is unable to metabolise sugar properly; the result is hypoglycaemia. This low blood sugar condition is in fact responsible for many of the debilitating, and sometimes frightening, symptoms of PMT—headaches, fainting, weakness, irritability, aggressiveness and panic attacks. The worse the hypoglycaemia, the more severe the symptoms. Once menstruation occurs, sugar tolerance goes back to normal, the hypoglycaemia disappears and so do all the symptoms. Glucose tolerance tests made on women when they are pre-menstrual, and repeated later in the month, can produce astoundingly different results. Mood swings, angry outbursts and uncontrollable weepiness are all caused by a metabolism and hormones which have gone haywire.

So diet is important to correct this condition of low blood sugar. The best regime is six meals a day: three of moderate size and three snacks, with no long gaps between meals. Fasting at these times is inadvisable and so is drastic dieting, although a careful watch on one's weight adds to a general feeling of well-being. Some dieting can, in fact, aggravate the situation: fats are essential for hormone production, so eliminating them for a time can upset the menstrual cycle. Most food should be taken in the form of complex carbohydrates and high protein foods: these take longer to be converted into glucose, and therefore they provide the body with a constant supply of sugar to the bloodstream. Also, these foods are higher in vitamins, minerals and fibre than highly processed foods.

Carbohydrates

Carbohydrates can be divided into two types, simple and complex; both are digested and become glucose. The simple carbohydrates break down fast into glucose—examples of these are sugar and milk. The complex carbohydrates are found in fruit, vegetables and grains; some parts of the grain (such as bran) are almost non-digestible and they act as roughage. These complex carbohydrates are what we should eat at regular intervals to prevent us suffering from low blood sugar. White sugar, white flour, white pasta and white rice, etc should be avoided; the vitamin B content is much greater in the brown, less processed varieties.

Our intake of caffeine in tea and coffee should be reduced as much as possible, and salt should be avoided if water retention occurs. Sodium is already present in many manufactured products (such as processed, pickled foods and cured meats), but it is also found in some fresh vegetables such as spinach and celery.

In a booklet by Guy E. Abraham, called *Premenstrual Blues* (recommended by Dr James Dobson, Director of Focus on the Family), the following observations are made:

> If you are under a lot of stress and eat a lot of refined sugar, two things happen. Stress changes the levels of certain enzymes in the brain which creates a relative deficiency of dopamine, a brain substance involved in sedation. The highly refined sugar you eat forces tryptophan into your brain cells where it is converted to serotonin. Too much serotonin causes nervous tension: combine stress with high intake of refined sugar and you get a vicious cycle. The refined sugar triggers insulin release but in excess of what is needed. The refined

sugar increases the ability of insulin to act by three-
to eleven-fold. All of this results in lowering your
blood sugar, which stimulates the appetite centre
of your brain.

Now why chocolate? Chocolate is relatively rich
in magnesium. Without magnesium, you can't break
down sugar to get energy from it. This craving for
chocolate may be a sign of magnesium deficiency.
Chocolate is also rich in phenylethylamine, a sub-
stance similar to dopamine. This craving for chocolate could be an instinctual drive to crave for the
substances in which one is deficient.

Excess refined carbohydrates trigger insulin release in excess. Insulin is known to prevent the
kidneys from excreting sodium (salt). The salt and
water retention is in part an insulin effect. In
most women with PMT, craving for sweets and
subsequent ingestion of large amounts of refined
carbohydrates precede the swelling, and weight
gain, which seems to confirm the role of refined
sugar-triggered insulin release as the cause of PMT.
Poor nutrition decreases resistance to stress. Stress
by itself causes the adrenal glands to release in
the blood increased amounts of salt-retaining hormones which potentiates the salt-retaining effect of
insulin.

Supplements

Vitamin and mineral supplements are part of the
overall treatment plan. Vitamin B6 taken as part of
a B complex is a great help to many women, as
is extra calcium. The foodstuffs we eat contain
vitamins and minerals, of course, but we need to

be careful in our selection and take supplements if necessary.

Vitamin E is a valuable vitamin necessary to women in middle age, as without it bones can become brittle.

Evening Primrose Oil is one of the most recently discovered aids, recommended by St Thomas' Hospital. I have been using it for several years, with considerable success: headaches are much less troublesome and my mood changes are much more moderate. This oil comes from a wild flower, and it provides the body with Gammalinolenic acid. It is thought that some women could be deficient in this and there are certainly encouraging signs as research is beginning to show. One form of this, under the trade names 'Efamol' and 'Efavite', can be a useful vitamin and mineral combination. In 1983, of sixty-five women treated with oil of primrose only fifteen per cent said they felt no better, while all the rest found considerable easing of their discomforts. The company producing the oil prefers not to invest in much advertising. They believe the product will speak for itself and they prefer to plough profits back into further production.

Human breast milk contains GLA, so Evening Primrose Oil is now being called 'mother's milk for adults'. It is now recognised by the British Pharmaceutical Society and it can be obtained on prescription in certain cases, as it helps many other medical conditions such as damaged liver in alcoholics, eczema, arthritis, hyperactivity in children, etc.

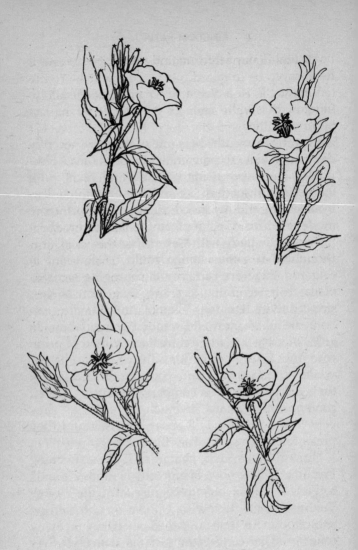

Evening Primrose

All this dietary information shows how careful we have to be to guard our bodies, which are the temple of the Holy Spirit. If we fail to eat sensibly, thinking that we're saving money; if we let the rest of the family have the good food while we eat leftovers, we are not being fair to our systems; in any case it is a false economy.

We should be aware of the dangers of junk foods, with their high sugar content. Additives in food are another source of danger, useful for the manufacturers to make money (enabling products to have a longer shelf life) but in the long term potentially dangerous to our bodies. There is ample evidence that certain food additives are undesirable in the context of allergic changes near the menstrual period. The whole subject of correct nutrition can make a valuable study for our women's groups and be a lifetime's interest. We are the ones who choose the food and the menus for our families, and as good stewards we are responsible for keeping our bodies and those of our families in good working order.

Water retention

The bloatedness we feel before a period is caused by fluid retention, the fluid especially collecting in damaged tissue. It is wise, therefore, to cut down on fluids at this time, and to avoid salt as much as possible. There are diuretic tablets available on prescription and over the counter, though these should be used with care; herbal ones are available, too. Some foods have a natural diuretic function; they include parsley, cucumber, celery, watercress, water melon, parsnips and strawberries. Strong coffee also acts as a diuretic, but you have to weigh up that advantage against the disadvantage that coffee draws on your body's supply of vitamin B6 in order to be digested. Decaffeinated coffee is no better from this point of view, and the chemicals involved in the process of decaffeination may make it worse!

Using diuretics can cause potassium loss which leads to muscle weakness, intestinal problems and constipation. To counteract this loss we need foods rich in potassium, which include oranges, figs, bananas, tomatoes and apricots.

Milk, eggs and cheese provide calcium and eating those may help with the stomach cramps and perhaps other aspects of PMT.

Exercise

This is something most of us fail to do, yet for all-round health we neglect it at our peril. Housework, although active and tiring, isn't sufficient exercise for our whole body. Cycling, walking, swimming, skipping and aerobics (with care) are better, giving all our muscles work and usually fresh air as well.

There are special exercises for tense muscles, some of which are described in some of the books in the Bibliography. A regular exercise plan is good, such as *Physical Fitness, A Twelve-Minute-a-Day Plan for Women* (Penguin Books): this is neither exhausting nor time consuming. The books, tapes and videos by Rosemary Conley are very good.

Lethargic Syndrome

Grooming

> 'She is clothed with strength and dignity' (Prov 31:25).
> 'Not merely in the outward appearance' (1 Pet 3:3
> AMPLIFIED).

Just as we are instructed not to make a show
of it when we fast, so too, when we are feeling
low, we needn't broadcast it by looking unkempt
and miserable. To make ourselves look smart will
also be a good morale booster. So we should wash
our hair more often, use make-up tastefully (to
literally 'make up' the deficiency) and wear our
favourite smart clothes, probably the loose fitting
ones.

One thing that has emerged recently is the
colour analysis that teaches what shades of colours
best suit us. We all come into one of four categories
which is judged by hair, eyes and skin tone. One
book, *Colour Me Beautiful* by Carole Jackson says,
'Why look good when you can look terrific?'

Putting these theories into practice can produce
a remarkable change in our overall appearance,
and of course it does wonderful things for our
morale.

Alternative medicine

Beware of the hidden dangers in this field. *Healing
at any Price* is a good book to consult, as it covers

various therapies that are popular today and examines them in the light of biblical truth. The problems resulting from our involvement with some of these therapies can be much more complicated than mere hormonal imbalance.

6
Kingdom Pacing

'You know when I sit and when I rise' (Ps 139:2).

You don't need to be reminded that stress aggravates pre-menstrual problems. It is important to look ahead and see how to avoid unnecessary pressures at these times. Why set up a high-stress meeting on a day when you may be particularly sensitive to stress, or arrange to counsel someone with deep needs—or, down at the nitty-gritty level, why plan to do some household job that requires concentration and precision and upheaval?

Keep your work up to date, and learn to pace yourself. Go ahead with your daily responsibilities though, however you feel—God honours obedience. Keep surfaces clear and tidy. It may be that part of our problem is that we lack those slow therapeutic activities like beating carpets, scrubbing, or rubbing clothes clean by peaceful flowing rivers. The present trend for making our own wholemeal bread helps fulfil something in us as we busily knead it! The modern pace of life here in the West seems to have aggravated stress problems. Good brisk walks and digging the garden can help, by providing exercise and relaxation.

Don't make crucial commitments or decisions at this time if possible. Arrange to rest each day if you can, and have treats to look forward to—reading the paper (did I say avoid stress?), having an absorbing book to read, a creative hobby that doesn't require too much concentration. Listen to good music, both classical and the lovely worship songs that the Lord has been giving us in such abundance. Spend time with positive people, who don't drain you; find friends who provide supportive fellowship at these times.

Professor T. Jeffcoate in *The Standard Textbook on Clinical Gynaecology* says,

> The most important line of treatment is the correction of environmental cause factors. A sympathetic enquiry into personal problems and worries and a reasonable explanation of the situation to both the patient and her husband may do more good than any specific medical remedies. Since the woman is overdriving herself nervously, if not physically, reorganisation of her life or her outlook on life is often necessary. A sleep for two hours in the middle of every day is particularly useful.

As we live closely together in the Kingdom community we must watch each other and lovingly offer counsel in each other's lives if we see a

Creativity Syndrome

stressful situation being set up. Find ways to advise one another before the crash rather than (to change the metaphor) shut the door when the horse has bolted!

Some husbands or friends actually list jobs so that a woman can learn to discipline and pace herself and learn to make her own daily schedule. Daily, weekly and monthly goals help; to write down what needs doing is often half the battle.

A word to friends

You may wonder how best to help a close friend who is going through these experiences. Make a mental note of her dates, if that is possible; recognise a pattern, anyway, and be extra alert and thoughtful. Pray for her and notice Scriptures you can share with her.

A timely phone call or (better still) a visit could be an encouragement; if possible, suggest a pleasant outing or activity together. Be positive in your conversation, and don't encourage a 'pity party'. If your relationship is suitable, and if she has no other help, set her tasks to do and let her report on her progress—and work with her if possible.

Don't encourage any critical spirit, or take personally any rejection; encouragement is the key word. Any praise that comes my way I return to the Lord, as part of my daily sacrifice, for he is the one who enables me; but I also store up the praise and remind myself of it when I feel worthless and inadequate. Too much sympathy is not always

Irritability, Tension, Anxiety Syndrome

helpful: be positive but not too boisterous! Don't get intensely spiritual and call a prayer meeting; rather, use humour and remind her that the blackness will pass. If possible, get her out of the house for a walk—exercise is therapeutic.

When your friend is well, remind her of these good times and encourage her to get ahead with responsibilities. Check that she's eating sensibly and getting time for recreation. Encourage her to get medical help if you are at all concerned about the degree of hormone imbalance you observe.

7
A Word to Men

'Husbands, in the same way be considerate with your wives' (1 Pet 3:7).

'You married men should live considerately with your wives with an intelligent recognition (of the married relation), honouring the woman as (physically) the weaker but realising that you are joint heirs of the grace (God's unmerited favour) of life, in order that your prayers may not be hindered and cut off—otherwise you cannot pray effectively' (1 Pet 3:7 AMPLIFIED).

This chapter is mainly addressed to husbands, but some of it will clearly apply to any man who works alongside women.

The apostle Peter has already said some challenging things to the wives before he commences his advice to husbands. Many a husband can identify with Professor Higgins in Pygmalion who says with a heavy sigh, 'Why can't a woman be more like a man?' You probably are wiser than the professor because you know the fascination involved in getting to understand the unpredictable nature of a woman—and you know these variations are related to the hormonal changes.

You are only too aware that at times you are public enemy number one, the target for her angry outbursts. 'You always' and 'you never' are phrases frequently used by your wife, or the women you work with. If you are wise you will recognise a pattern related to her monthly cycle: if she is always negative and hostile, then that is a different matter.

As husbands and wives who love each other and want to please each other, you know that premenstrual tension is one of the biggest strains on a couple. If there were obvious physical signs we would remember to make allowances, but so much goes on deep inside a woman, invisibly. Similarly, we repress our feelings so much that it is inevitable that our emotions will boil over from time to time. Then there is the monotony of it occurring month after month. There must be embarrassment for a husband whose wife is 'behaving badly'; he has his hurt feelings to handle, he may see the look of surprise on friends' faces, he may see the startled look on the children's faces when they are sharply spoken to by their mother. A husband has to go to work with the memory of a tear-stained face or hostile words ringing in his ear. Unlike a woman, he is unlikely to betray his wife by confiding in another friend. He knows, too, that with all the other pressures he handles, this is the last thing he wants monotonously dogging the footsteps of his marriage. It is understandable if he sometimes retaliates in a less than Christlike manner. But then he remembers that unless he lives 'considerately' with his wife, his prayers could be hindered, so he seeks to learn and understand the ways of a woman, knowing that will improve his marriage and make his praying effective.

What are the main symptoms of PMT that affect a husband?

Aggression has already been mentioned. There is the tearfulness—very hard for a man to handle. Sometimes the wife herself does not know why she is crying, which complicates things further!

Depression and low self-esteem are very much related to pre-menstrual tension. The depression is part of the hormone change taking place. Low self-esteem is complicated by weight gain, which makes the woman feel fat and unattractive. Skin blemishes also occur at this time, which again add to the factors contributing to depression. The husband needs to reassure his wife that he loves her and that she is important to him. The natural tendency is to back off and keep away, but that is not the most helpful action. Bring flowers, help more with the chores, take the children off her hands—these are the ways to say 'I love you' at these times.

Confusion and clumsiness, forgetfulness and restlessness, are other manifestations, and all can be very annoying when you are living with such a person.

Loss of Self-Esteem Syndrome

Wives appreciate it if husbands look into these symptoms and try to understand. Help her to find solutions through eating more correctly and exercising; help her to plan her schedule; go to an understanding doctor with her. The doctor can confirm the diagnosis of pre-menstrual tension— its cyclical nature is sure proof. You can help your wife carry out the doctor's advice and use any medical help he may give her.

Remember, too, that this is not the real woman you fell in love with and married. You are seeing her trying to handle chemical imbalance. Think of the good times, the fun and laughter, the creativity, the good ideas your wife comes up with. It is said that it is the creative, imaginative woman who is more likely to suffer this tension!

Another word of warning: remember that, when she comes out of this cycle, she will be on top again. She won't need your support in the same way and this may bewilder you and hurt your feelings. You may feel threatened because you are not needed in the same way with this change of control centre.

You may find it necessary to have some counselling. Jay Adams, a specialist in biblical counselling, has written a little pamphlet on the subject, but there are various resources you could draw on to get support for your wife in this way.

God's word often comes alive to us in times of need, when we call on him in prayer.

For no temptation—no trial regarded as enticing to sin [no matter how it comes or where it leads]—has overtaken you and laid hold on you that is not common to man—that is, no temptation or trial has come to you that is beyond human resistance and that is not adjusted and adapted and belonging to human experience, and such as man can bear. But God is faithful [to His Word and to His compassionate nature], and He [can be trusted] not to let you be tempted and tried and assayed beyond your ability and strength of resistance and power to endure, but with the temptation He will [always] also provide the way out—the means of escape to a landing place—that you may be capable and strong and powerful patiently to bear up under it (1 Cor 10:13 AMPLIFIED).

Paul might have been writing this to husbands of pre-menstrual wives, it is all so appropriate!

All trials and tests can be used in our character-forming by the Lord, and this strain in a marriage can develop you as a man. Cry out to God and seek his strength and his solutions, and as you act out your headship and governing role towards your wife in her need, she is the more secure and more protected. There is nothing worse than a spoilt wife whose husband gives in to her every whim and yields to her every mood. By steering her through these times and channelling her creative ideas, you are yourself gaining tremendous experience and skills. Timothy says this is one of the qualities of an elder: 'He must manage his own family well' (1 Tim 3:4).

You will obviously be praying for her, but do pray *with* her at these times. Spiritually, she may be feeling that God is far away, she may feel that she is condemned and a failure before him, so lead her into God's presence. Be sensitive in the way you pray and the words you use! Read the Bible to her, prayerfully selecting passages that will build her up and assure her of God's love. Regular Bible reading and prayer together will prepare the way for these special times of need.

Tim LaHaye in *Spirit Controlled Family*, speaking on 'What is Love?' says,

> True love is patient and enduring; a good test is how you respond to your wife during her menstrual cycle. She needs extra love and tender warmth at a time when she may be less lovable. He's a wise husband who anticipates the time of the month or any other of his wife's pressure points and goes out of his way to show love regardless of her attitude.

Ingrid Trobish in *The Joy of Being a Woman* has a helpful chapter in this connection. She says that a wise husband will understand why, at times, his wife is sad and irritated without apparent cause. He knows she is steered by her emotions, so he sees things in the right perspective and can respond with 'understanding silence'!

In *Wedding Vows* written by Dr W.J. Ern Baxter there is included the question, 'Will you wash her with your words of praise and gratitude, that she

Crying Syndrome

might live securely in your love, and will you listen to her with full attention and patiently absorb her emotion?'

The fact that you have taken time to read this is a step in the right direction.

But listen, wives!

Lest we turn into spoilt brats who can literally get away with murder because of the excuse of pre-menstrual tension, we wives must act responsibly. It is only fair to share with husbands when the stressful time is approaching and not to expect them to read our minds. In this way we enable them to show more understanding and care for our needs.

God has made husbands as our heads and protectors, and they are responsible to God in the way they care for us. We must be sensitive to their pressures, such as relationships at work, respons-ibilities, rivalry, travel in traffic, strikes, threat of redundancy, the cost of living and so on. We must be alert to their health needs.

Many of us have labour-saving homes, which under God our husbands have been pleased to provide, but we are in danger of using the time we have saved in fretting at home and 'urging and impelling' the men as they walk in from a stressful day. If we go out to work, we can make impossible demands on them in domestic duties.

The wise woman who wants to preserve her husband will take his day into account. She can run the home wisely to free him from many pressures. By keeping it clean and tidy and ordered as she plans her day, she can be rested and refreshed when he comes home. The home is then a haven, providing good food and quietness. She can share things from the Bible to refresh him spiritually. If a wife gives all that lovingly to her husband she will reap a handsome reward in terms of peace and understanding. Let us resist being pushed into the world's mould, but be all that God meant us to be as homemakers.

In like manner you married women, be submissive to your own husbands—subordinate yourselves as being secondary to and dependent on them, and adapt yourselves to them. So that even if any do not obey the Word [of God], they may be won over not by discussion but by the [godly] lives of their wives, when they observe the pure and modest way in which you conduct yourselves, together with your reverence [for your husband. That is, you are to feel for him all that reverence includes]—to respect, defer to, revere him; [revere means] to honour, esteem (appreciate, prize), and [in the human sense] adore him; [and adore means] to admire, praise, be devoted to, deeply love and enjoy [your husband].

Let not yours be the [merely] external adorning with [elaborate] interweaving and knotting of the hair, the wearing of jewellery, or changes of clothes; but let it be the inward adorning and beauty of the hidden person of the heart, with the incorruptible and unfading charm of a gentle and peaceful spirit, which (is not anxious or wrought up, but) is very precious in the sight of God. For it was thus that the pious women of old who hoped in God were [accustomed] to beautify themselves, and were submissive to their husbands—adapting themselves to them as themselves secondary and dependent upon them.

It was thus that Sarah obeyed Abraham [following his guidance and acknowledging his headship over her by] calling him lord—master, leader, authority. And you are now her true daughters if you do right and let nothing terrify you—not giving way to hysterical fears or letting anxieties unnerve you.

(1 Pet 3:1–6 AMP).

A Conversation, Too Often Unspoken,
Written by a Husband
Imagining His Wife's Feelings

I just want to know that you love me.
I've been niggly, ill at ease today,
Moody, I suppose.
Short and sharp with the children.
Do you still love me?
Even though I'm not so sweet.

Sometimes I feel unfulfilled at home,
Cabbage-like, some would say.
I feel life has passed me by.
I know you appreciate my work,
My creative care,
And express it with a gift, a gentle look
. . . but am I really all you say?

Last week I sparkled, played on top,
Even danced a little
. . . but now, the rising prices,
That old settee, a rusting car,
All cloud around cyclonic-like.

Yes, I know the doctor says I'll be all right
In a day or two
But sometimes it seems to drag on for so long.
Goodnight, dear.
Thanks for listening, understanding.

Lord, now my love's asleep.
You made me, you must understand.
I feel controlled, hormone conditioned.
Help me to rise with eagle's wings,
Soaring above my bloated, flesh-bound feelings.
Renew my strength, my patient tranquil love,
Renew my mind . . . as I wait on you.

8

Kingdom Seeking

'If anyone is in Christ, he is a new creation' (2 Cor 5:17).

I am aware that some people who read this may be left feeling bewildered, because they do not understand what it means to know God in such a personal way. It is because we love God that we want to live a daily life that is pleasing to him, speaking to him in prayer as he speaks to us from his word; we want to do our daily tasks to his glory.

As you can see, there is no instant formula to deliver us from PMT, but with full confidence I can share the very good news of the wonderful way God has planned for us to get to know him. You may already know the verse from John's Gospel, 3:16: 'For God so loved the world that he gave his one and only Son, that whoever believes in him shall not perish but have eternal life.'

We are a part of this world that God loves, and the everlasting life can begin now—life of a different quality and dimension from the ordinary life we know. The irritability, the resentment, the bitterness and self pity in our lives can be forgiven, for Christ died for these sins. He rose again and by the power of the Holy Spirit he lives in us and develops in us a nature of increasing holiness. God is interested in developing our characters.

I see this happening in my own life, although there was a time when I had no personal faith, and thought it was presumptuous to say that one knew God in such a way. I see Christ's lordship working in the lives of the women around me, as Jesus said in John 10:10 'I am come that they may have life, and have it to the full.'

This is a promise from the Lord Jesus to make us fulfilled women, functioning in ways that enrich our lives and the lives of those around us. Women experiencing the life of Christ within are a great asset in our local community.

In the next chapter I include a prayer, among the other prayers that have been written, that you can use to enable you to reach out to God in faith. God says, 'You will seek me and find me when you seek me with all your heart' (Jer 29:13). Ask for help, and any Christian should be able to help you find a personal faith for yourself.

'I've begun, but is there more to the Christian life?'

'Be filled with the Spirit' (Eph 5:18).

In researching and counselling I have noticed that

women who are filled with the Holy Spirit have a greater resilience than those who are not. The power promised in Acts 1:8 surely applies to this area of our life—although we may find that the warfare hots up when we mean business with God and ask to be filled with the Holy Spirit.

Many of us haven't entered into the full gospel as described by Peter on the day of Pentecost. The moving of the Spirit in these days and the renewal he brings show us clearly where we stand. 'He has filled the hungry with good things, but has sent the rich away empty' (Lk 1:53).

The fruit of the Spirit is very important and can be produced as we tackle our monthly trials, but the gifts of the Spirit must not be overlooked: 'Speak to one another with psalms, hymns and spiritual songs. Sing and make music in your heart to the Lord' (Eph 5:19); all this helps in the overall victory. Both the gift of prophecy and the laying on of hands for healing have brought me great assurance.

We cannot get along on one cylinder or in our own strength; I have seen too many lives transformed after the filling of the Holy Spirit, to ignore his most valuable ministry. 'Got it all at conversion? I ask you in God's name where is it?' said Dr Martyn Lloyd-Jones. For those still seeking this experience or who as yet don't fully understand it, a very helpful booklet, *The Baptism in the Holy Spirit*, listed in the Bibliography, is available from:

New Covenant Church,
West Street Christian Centre,
Dunstable,
Beds
LU6 1SX.

9
Talking to God About Our Needs

Most of these prayers were written by various PMT sufferers.

A prayer you could use if you want to come to know God

O God, I don't know You very well,
but I want to know You.
My heart tells me that there is more to life than
this and I've sensed the wonder of how You can
help me in coping with my pre-menstrual tension.
I'm tired of struggling on my own.
Help me to get to know You. Help me to understand
the Bible and learn to speak to You in prayer.
Help me to find a group of people who know You
personally so I can learn from them. Amen.

Jesus, come closer now to me
I am reaching out for You, I need to see

No more just words and facts about
A man who lived long ago.
Jesus, it's You I really need to know.

Father, You know how I'm feeling,
You know that I've looked away from You again
and started to look in on myself.
Father, forgive me. Please give me the grace
really to turn around and surrender to You afresh.
Please enable me to walk steadfastly with You;
to rise above the things that are going on in me
and to know myself seated in the heavenly places with
   You,
where I can reign in today's circumstances.

Father, I praise You for Your love.
I praise You that through You I can do all things.
I can know Your presence today,
I can walk victoriously with You
as I rest in Your love
and allow You to have control over my day.
Father, I bless You
for all that You are teaching me at this time,
for the opportunity I have today to live victoriously.
Thank You for cleansing me and filling me with Your
   Spirit.
Thank You for all You are doing in me. Amen.

Thank You, Lord,
that we are fearfully and wonderfully made.
Your creation is so glorious and complex
beyond our understanding.
In all Your creation we are precious to You
and You hold us in Your hand.
Thank You that You know how we feel at this time,
that You are patient with us,
that You pick us up again and again.

Lord, You understand the way my body works
so much better than I do,
and it's so comforting for me
to be able to turn to You,
knowing that You have the solution for me.
I am asking You now, Lord, to take over for me
where I have failed so miserably
in fighting this battle month by month with my
    hormones.
Begin to prepare my body now, Lord,
so that when the time comes, next week,
I can go forth in confidence,
knowing that Your loving hand is upon me.
Prepare the week for me, Lord,
unravelling it, taking the knots of complications
and harassment which were in store,
smoothing the way for me,
so that my life may continue to give glory to Your name.

Dear Lord, I've got butterflies in my stomach again
and there is nothing to be nervous of. My neck and

shoulders are aching from tension and I've nothing to be tense about. I want to scream and cry, but I have nothing to cry about. I want to smack the children, but they haven't been naughty. I want to tell my husband what a good-for-nothing he is, but he isn't.

Are You there, Lord? This heaviness of mind, this bloating of the body, this depression of spirit is pulling me away from You, Lord, and it's all to do with hormones. I'll be all right next week but now, Lord, it's up to You. Here I am, please take me and all my problems that don't really exist. Forgive me, Lord, for fighting in my own strength and losing. Thank You, Lord, for giving me peace in turmoil, order in my confusion, reassurance in my bewilderment and a total answer in all my questioning.

It shows no care
denies despair
It will not share
the fear and worry there—
My Sunday face

Anxiety
the smiling mouth belies
You can see
If you look beyond the eyes
But bravely, foolishly
my face denies
my need of you

It would be such disgrace
to let you see behind
my Sunday face

I said to the Lord,
'You see before You
A woman worn and torn,
A pale shadow of what I was
Before You led me through the storm.'
And this was His reply:
'I see a heart seeking after Me
A hand, strengthened now,
That placed itself in Mine,
And feet that followed, though unwillingly;
A loving and a more compassionate face
Willing to press on and win the race
What's more, I see what you one day will be.'

10

A Final Word of Testimony

'We can comfort those in any trouble with the comfort we ourselves have received from God' (2 Cor 1:4).

I have personally found both challenge and relief in writing this book. I still wonder why I don't put into practice all I know, but each time I'm under stress in this way, I learn many lessons. I learn of God's unending forgiveness and his understanding heart. I learn of the power he can put to work in my life. I see how the enemy would use my condition to attack my ministry, but I see, too, the way my spiritual senses are sharpened and I can grow closer to the Lord.

I'm not preoccupied with the problem of PMT, but again and again it emerges in conversation with other women, showing how widespread the symptoms are.

I have gained considerable relief by prayer, laying on of hands, ministry, and taking the practical steps outlined in these pages. I find it useful at times to speak out and rebuke the self-pity or resentment that I feel building up, and then I praise God. In this way I'm learning to hate sin as God does and so bring his judgement upon it.

At times in the past I have scolded and punished myself, but now I've come to see that for me it is a question of health. So I seek to live along biblical lines so that my soul is thriving, and trust that with correct diet and exercise this aspect of my health will improve. I pray the same for you.

'Older women . . . train the younger women . . .' (Tit 2:3–4). God's purpose is to have balanced, mature women functioning in the community, able to train and advise the younger women in all sorts of ways. By doing this they relieve the pastors of much work and potential temptation.

If hormonal imbalance is 'knocking them down like flies', women are not the army the Lord means them to be; but if they have gained victory in this area by all the means at their disposal, they can be effective for the Kingdom of God. Menopausal problems of loneliness, the 'empty nest' syndrome, feelings of uselessness, and many of the physical symptoms can be alleviated if the measures described in this book are taken earlier on in a woman's life.

'Charm is deceptive, and beauty is fleeting; but a woman who fears the Lord is to be praised. Give her the reward she has earned, and let her works bring her praise at the city gate' (Prov 31:30–31).

Practical Countdown

1. Prepare by prayer.
2. Have Scriptures at hand that you can think about as promises.
3. Get up to date with as much work as possible.
4. If it helps, write out schedules: meal plans, order of work, etc.
5. Inform those you live with of the time of month, perhaps by faces on the calendar. 🙂 🙁
6. Eat sensibly—keep up with vitamins.
7. Get exercise.
8. Get sleep.
9. Recognise negative thoughts and capture them.
10. Think positively.
11. Do something for someone else.
12. Wear loose fitting clothes at this time.
13. Pamper yourself a little, for instance with hot baths.
14. Remind yourself that it won't last for long.

Bibliography

Abraham, Guy E. *Pre-Menstrual Blues*. Focus on the Family: Arcadia, CA, 1980.

Adams, Jay. *Competent to Counsel*. Baker Book House: Grand Rapids, Michigan, 1970.

Brush, Dr Michael. *Understanding Pre-Menstrual Tension*. Pan Books, 1984.

Bilheimer, Paul. *Don't Waste Your Sorrows*. Kingsway: Eastbourne, 1983.

Chapian, Marie and Neva Coyle *Free to be Slim*. Kingsway: Eastbourne, 1985.

Dalton, Dr Katharina. *Once a Month*. Fontana: 1978.

Davis, Adele. *Let's Get Well*. Unwin, 1966.

Dobson, Dr James. *Man to Man About Women*. Kingsway: Eastbourne, 1975.

Graham, Judy. *Evening Primrose Oil*. Thorsons: Wellingborough, 1984.

Harrison, Dr Michelle. *Self-Help with PMS*. Macdonald: London, 1982.

Heller, Dr A.L. *Your Body His Temple*. Thomas Nelson: Nashville, 1981.

Houghton, John. *The Healthy Alternative*. Kingsway: Eastbourne, 1985.

Jasper, Rick. *Fit and Free*. Regal G/L Publications: Glendale, California, 1978.

Jebb, Stanley. *Baptism in the Holy Spirit*. New Covenant Church: Dunstable, 1973.

Lever, Judy. *PMT: The Unrecognised Illness*. New English Library: London, 1979.

Nazzaro, Dr Ann, and Lombard, Dr Donald, with Horrobin, Dr David *The PMT Solution*. Adamantine Press: London, 1985.

Nelson, Timothy. *The Head Covering*. Mourne Missionary Trust: Kilkeel, N Ireland.

Pfeifer, Samual. *Healing at Any Price?* Word: Milton Keynes, 1980.

Shreeve, Dr Caroline. *The Pre-Menstrual Syndrome*. Thorsons: Wellingborough.

Sneed, Sharon M., and McIlhaney, Joe S. *PMS: What It Is and What You Can Do About It*. Baker Book House: Grand Rapids, Michigan, 1988.

Triangle, Jean Brand. *A Woman's Privilege*. SPCK, 1985.

What In The World Is God Saying About Women?

by Christine Noble

A woman's place is...where?

And on this point Christians are in crisis. The feminists struggle for leadership—others insist this role is for men only.

In her own dynamic and refreshing way Christine Noble shows how women can take their rightful place in God's plan for our generation.

'Christine Noble's comments are always articulate and exciting! She writes in the same way, and this book is both stimulating and provocative. You may not always agree with what she says, but it will certainly make you think. Compulsive reading and definitely a book not to be missed.'

CLIVE CALVER
General Director, Evangelical Alliance

CHRISTINE NOBLE is a well-known international speaker and Christian leader who works with Team Spirit based in Romford, Essex. She and John have been married for 32 years, and they have five children and seven grandchildren.

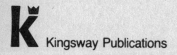

Kingsway Publications

Women Set Free

by Wendy Virgo

Through the centuries women have yearned for freedom—from oppression and tyranny, from poverty and pain. But again and again we have failed to realise that fundamentally we are enslaved *within*. Freedom must begin on the inside with the discovery of peace with God.

Yet even as Christians we find many 'enemies' seeking to block our freedom.

Wendy Virgo exposes some of these enemies—inner attitudes of guilt, low self-image, bitterness—and shows how we can learn to enjoy our freedom in Christ. She also faces the controversial issue of authority in the church and explains how women can find freedom, security and fulfilment in playing their part in bringing in the kingdom of God.

WENDY VIRGO is also the author of *Leading Ladies*, and a speaker based with New Frontiers International. She is married to Terry and they have five children.

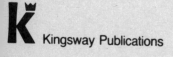

Kingsway Publications

Stress

by Gaius Davies

Stress is built into modern life. With sweeping changes in society and technology, our lives move more frantically than ever.

Are Christians immune to stress? Dr Gaius Davies tackles the question head on: 'We are not, as Christian believers, exempt from any of the stresses that affect anyone else. Our faith is not a passport to freedom from pressures.' He shows why *Christians should never be afraid of seeking professional help*.

Using numerous examples from his many years' experience in clinical practice, Dr Davies examines the causes of breakdown and the many sources of stress which exist today: bereavement, guilt, personality problems, sexual tensions and the perennial problem of anxiety.

He demonstrates how modern medical knowledge can help, while recognising that some afflictions can only be healed spiritually.

A book that encourages those suffering from breakdown or stress, prevents others from succumbing to it, and offers invaluable help to all counsellors.

Dr Gaius Davies, FRCPsych, M Phil, DPM, is a Consultant Psychiatrist at a leading London teaching hospital and has served as Chairman of the Division of Psychological Medicine. He has also lectured at the London Institute for Contemporary Christianity. He is married with four children.

Royalties from this book go to St Christopher's Hospice.

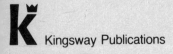

Kingsway Publications